D1200958

Ulysses S. Grant

*The remarkable true-life story
of the Civil War general
and peacetime President*

DRAMATIZED IN
ALL-PICTORIAL PRESENTATION

FOR IMPROVED
AWARENESS BOOK
READING

Davco Publishers
SKOKIE, ILLINOIS 60076

CONSULTANTS

SARA THROOP, PH.D.
Youngstown State University
Youngstown, Ohio

JOAN DUFF KISE, PH.D.
Elementary Education Department
Kent State University
Kent, Ohio

IDA S. MELTZER, B.A.
Supervisor Language Arts
Marine Park Junior High School
Brooklyn, New York

SYLVIA E. DAVIS, M.S.A.E.
Chairman Art Department
Waller High School
Chicago, Illinois

MORRIS R. BUSKE, M.A.
Instructor Social Studies
Department
Triton College
River Grove, Illinois

DOROTHY L. GROSS, B.S.M.S.
Instructor Art Department
Detroit Public Schools
Detroit, Michigan

CAROL SONNENBLICK, M.S.
Instructor Special Reading
Program
Staten Island Community
College
Staten Island, New York

EDITORIAL AND ART

Executive Editor
JANET TEGLAND, M.A.
Coordinator Learning
Disabilities Department
Top of the World School
Laguna Beach Unified School
District
Laguna Beach, California
Instructor Creative Writing
Saddleback Community College
Mission Viejo, California

Artists
STEVE DOBSON
MELVIN KEEFER
ROBERT GOLDIN
JANICE SALTZ

Historical Researchers
THOMAS MCLAUGHLIN
BARBARA MCCORMICK
BERTHA RABENS

Art and Editorial Production
HOWARD PARKS
CARYL KURTZMAN
ARLINE BLOCK
GAIL GOLDBERG
JOSEPH POSTILION
NICK CURCIO
HERBERT BUCHHOLZ
RONALD FALK

© MCMLXXVI Davco Publishers
Skokie, Illinois 60076

Library of Congress catalog card No. 75-12245
ISBN No. 0-89233-009-0

The true prosperity and greatness of a nation is to be found in the elevation and education of its laborers.

ULYSSES S. GRANT
Third Annual Message to Congress,
December, 1871

Table of Contents

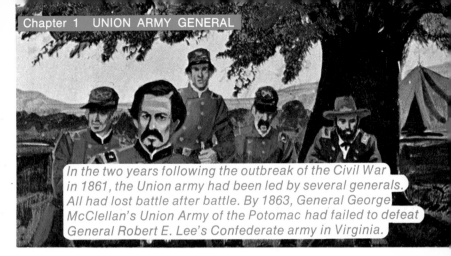

In the two years following the outbreak of the Civil War in 1861, the Union army had been led by several generals. All had lost battle after battle. By 1863, General George McClellan's Union Army of the Potomac had failed to defeat General Robert E. Lee's Confederate army in Virginia.

General Buell's Union army of the Ohio was driven back across Tennessee into Kentucky.

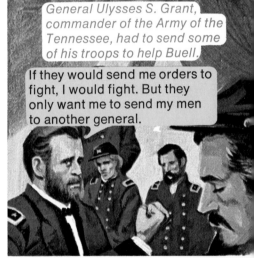

General Ulysses S. Grant, commander of the Army of the Tennessee, had to send some of his troops to help Buell.

If they would send me orders to fight, I would fight. But they only want me to send my men to another general.

One bright victory for the Union was Rear Admiral David Farragut's capture of the city of New Orleans.

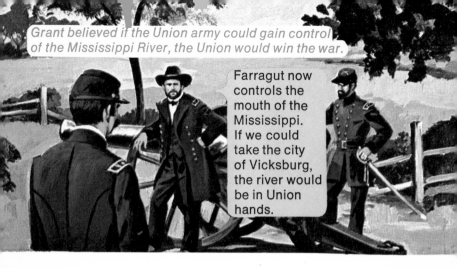

Grant believed if the Union army could gain control of the Mississippi River, the Union would win the war.

Farragut now controls the mouth of the Mississippi. If we could take the city of Vicksburg, the river would be in Union hands.

Halleck, the Union army commander in chief, finally agreed.

Tell General Grant to move his troops to the city of Jackson, Mississippi and prepare to attack Vicksburg from the east. General Sherman will attack from the north.

But the plan was plain to the Confederates. They moved fast, and burned Grant's supply depot to the ground.

And Sherman's army was driven back with many casualties.

Sound retreat!

6

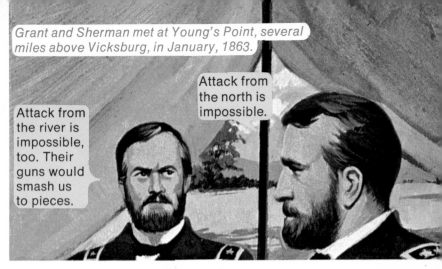

Grant and Sherman met at Young's Point, several miles above Vicksburg, in January, 1863.

Attack from the north is impossible.

Attack from the river is impossible, too. Their guns would smash us to pieces.

Grant spent all winter working on a secret military plan he hoped would surprise the enemy.

We must move our boats down the west side of the river until they are *below* Vicksburg. Then the infantry will march down the west bank. They will be transported across the river, and spread out to surround the city.

The Union boats began to move on the night of April 16, 1863.

All the Union boats were hit by the Vicksburg gun batteries—but only one was sunk.

We made it! All but one. We made it!

While Grant's men were marching down the west bank of the river . . .

. . . General Sherman attacked again to draw the attention of the Confederate army to him—and away from Grant.

Sherman is attacking, General Pemberton!

Then we shall drive him back again!

By the time the Confederates realized Sherman's attack was a trick—Grant's men had crossed the Mississippi.

By May 19, Grant's men had surrounded Vicksburg. Grant kept the city under siege for 47 days. The Confederate army was forced to surrender the city on July 4, 1863.

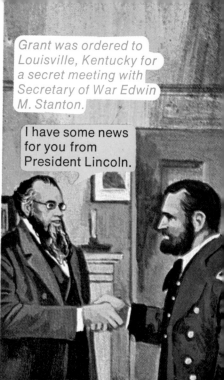

Grant was ordered to Louisville, Kentucky for a secret meeting with Secretary of War Edwin M. Stanton.

I have some news for you from President Lincoln.

You are to take command of the entire Union Army of the West.

You are to go at once to Chattanooga, Tennessee to save the Union troops there. They are surrounded by the Confederate army, and almost out of supplies.

Grant reached Chattanooga on October 24. He found that the army chief engineer had created a bold plan to reopen supply routes for the Union army.

With wood from this river, we can make pontoon bridges, Then we can cross the river for a surprise attack on Brown's Ferry.

Grant approved of the plan—

—and it worked.

Yankees! Where'd they come from?

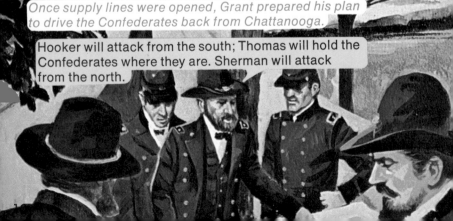

Once supply lines were opened, Grant prepared his plan to drive the Confederates back from Chattanooga.

Hooker will attack from the south; Thomas will hold the Confederates where they are. Sherman will attack from the north.

After three days of bitter fighting, the Confederates retreated into Georgia.

Grant's success brought him a gold medal from Congress.

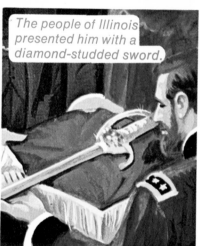

The people of Illinois presented him with a diamond-studded sword.

And President Lincoln named Grant lieutenant general of the Union army—the highest rank in the land.

Mr. President, I accept the commission with gratitude.

The Union army is in your hands. You will have a free hand, General Grant. Even *I* do not want to know your battle plans for fear—without meaning to—I might reveal them to the enemy.

Ulysses Grant, who was to lead the Union army to victory, and go on to become the eighteenth President of the United States, was born on April 27, 1822, in Point Pleasant, Ohio. His father, Jesse Grant, was a successful leather-maker.

Then we'd better find a proper name for him. He's a month old, and we still haven't decided.

I know this child is going to be a great man, Hannah. I just know it.

A family meeting was held. Everyone wrote his choice of names on a slip of paper, and placed them in a hat.

It's decided. We'll name him Hiram Ulysses.

But we'll call him Ulysses.

When Ulysses was a year old, his family moved to Georgetown, Ohio.

It's a fine house you've built for us, Jesse.

Jesse's tannery did so well in Georgetown, he began buying forest land so he could cut his own lumber. He opened a livery stable. Ulysses loved horses from the time he was able to walk.

Move him, Hannah! He'll be trampled!

No, he has a way with horses.

By the time he was seven, he could drive a team of horses to the creek for water.

When he was ten, he was breaking and training wild colts.

Grant's father sent Ulysses to a "subscription" school.

I'll pay $7 a semester for his schooling.

I'll see to it that your son will learn. You'll surely get your money's worth.

When Ulysses was sixteen, his father told him he should start learning the leather-tanning trade.

But I don't want to be a tanner. I'll work for you until I'm twenty-one—then I'll leave home.

Jesse was surprised, and angry.

What *do* you want to do?

Be a farmer, or a trader on the river.

Jesse was determined his son should do something important with his life. He wrote an Ohio congressman asking for an appointment to West Point for Ulysses.

He received a reply at Christmas time, telling him Ulysses had been accepted.

I'm not sure I want to be a soldier.

You must go. West Point can change your whole life.

14

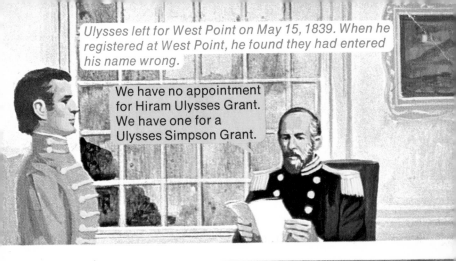

Ulysses left for West Point on May 15, 1839. When he registered at West Point, he found they had entered his name wrong.

We have no appointment for Hiram Ulysses Grant. We have one for a Ulysses Simpson Grant.

Grant went under the name of Ulysses Simpson Grant for the rest of his life.

I'm Will Sherman. And you're U. S. Grant, hm? Well, we'll call you Uncle Sam.

Grant and the other new cadets were "hazed" by the older cadets.

Repeat after me: ...I am an animal...

I am an animal...

Grant hated to drill. He had no ear for the rhythm of the drum beat.

15

During his second year at West Point, Grant became known as the best horseman at the academy.

He watched the new cadets entering West Point in 1842.

That's George McClellan. He's only fifteen years old.

That Thomas Jackson over there looks as green as I did three years ago.

During his last year, he shared a room with Frederick Dent from Missouri.

Ulysses kept improving his horsemanship. In the graduation exercises he set a new record for the high jump.

After graduation, Grant was assigned to serve as a second lieutenant with the Fourth Infantry at Jefferson Barracks, Missouri. He went to visit his roommate's family near St. Louis, Missouri.

Wait until you meet my sister, Julia. She's away at school now. She's *beautiful*.

Julia came home in February.

Your sister was right. You *are* beautiful.

Julia was also an excellent horsewoman.

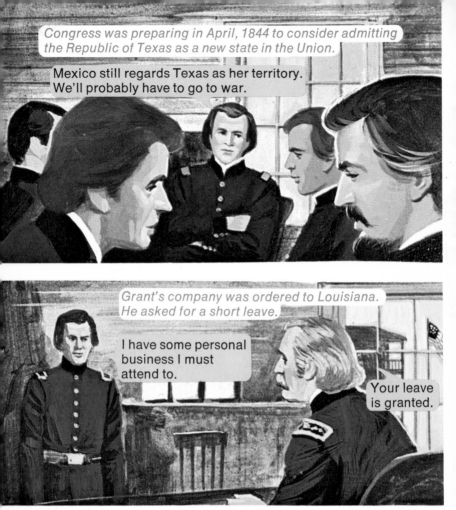

Congress was preparing in April, 1844 to consider admitting the Republic of Texas as a new state in the Union.

Mexico still regards Texas as her territory. We'll probably have to go to war.

Grant's company was ordered to Louisiana. He asked for a short leave.

I have some personal business I must attend to.

Your leave is granted.

I wanted to speak to you before I left for Louisiana. Will you marry me, Julia?

Yes, but we must keep our engagement a secret. My father does not want me to marry a soldier.

Congress approved annexation of Texas on March 1, 1845. Many believed that this would bring on war with Mexico. That summer, Grant's company was moved to Corpus Christi, Texas.

One of the leaders of the American army was General Zachary Taylor, known as Old Rough and Ready.

Taylor received orders from President Polk to build a fort on the Rio Grande, opposite the Mexican city of Matamoros.

We still haven't declared war, and neither has Mexico.

I don't like this war. I'm not sure we have a right to be here.

The American army reached the Rio Grande in March, 1846, and started to build a fort. Two months later, the Mexicans attacked. The expected war with Mexico began.

Grant and his men fought in high grass and brush. They helped win two battles . . .

. . . and Taylor's army seized the important town of Matamoros.

Meanwhile, the Mexicans were massing their army to fight at Monterrey—170 miles south.

The city of Monterrey was protected against attack by forts on the east, west, and north. A river blocked approach from the south. The American army attacked on September 20.

When soldiers in his company ran low on ammunition, Grant volunteered to ride for help.

After four days of hard fighting, the Mexican general surrendered.

Next, Grant's company was ordered to join General Winfield Scott's forces moving on Vera Cruz.

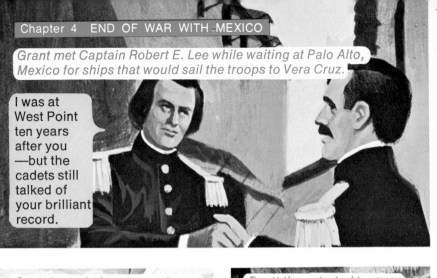

Grant met Captain Robert E. Lee while waiting at Palo Alto, Mexico for ships that would sail the troops to Vera Cruz.

I was at West Point ten years after you—but the cadets still talked of your brilliant record.

Scott brought heavy naval guns ashore to bombard Vera Cruz. The city fell in a month.

Scott then started to move his army toward the mountains—and the capital of Mexico, Mexico City.

Meanwhile, Mexican General Santa Anna massed his army to defend the city. He was considered a clever commander.

On a hill west of Mexico City stood a huge fortress, Chapultepec.

At the bottom of the hill was a mill called El Molino Del Rey.

Hundreds of cannon were ready on top of Chapultepec. They were aimed directly at the attacking American army.

The Americans attacked El Molino Del Rey on September 8, 1847. Grant was with the second attack force of soldiers.

23

Many American soldiers were cut down by a Mexican cannon located on top of the mill.

Grant knew that only a bold attack would knock out the cannon. Tipping up a cart and using it as a ladder, he stormed the hill . . .

. . . and captured the Mexican gun crew.

Mexico soon gave up El Molino Del Rey. Next, Grant's company entered Mexico City and slowly advanced, street by street.

Mexican soldiers fired from rooftops of buildings inside the city. They were picking off American soldiers as they advanced through the streets.

Again, Grant was called upon to halt the Mexican gunfire. He ordered a cannon lifted into the belfry of a church.

From the belfry, Grant directed the cannon fire against the Mexicans on the rooftops.

After a week of hard fighting, General Santa Anna retreated. On September 15, the American flag was raised in the central plaza of Mexico City.

The Treaty of Guadalupe Hidalgo ending the war was signed on March 10, 1848. America demanded California and Texas. Mexico also gave up land which later became Arizona, New Mexico, Nevada, and Colorado.

Grant's leadership during the war was quickly recognized by his superiors. He was promoted to first lieutenant for his bravery.

But his name was not included with the soldiers considered outstanding heroes of the Mexican War.

President Polk must be informed that these men fought brilliantly: Lee, McClellan, Bragg, and Sherman.

Grant returned to America in June, 1848.

Julia had waited four years for Grant to come home.

They were married on August 22, 1848.

Their first child was born in May, 1850.

We'll name him Frederick Dent Grant, after your father.

Grant was ordered in 1852, to report to his company, which was to leave for the Pacific Coast. Julia was expecting another child.

You must stay with my parents, Julia. I'll send for you later.

Grant was lonely and homesick at the quiet army outposts in Oregon and California.

I miss you very much, and long to see my newborn son.

To relieve his loneliness, he began to spend much of his time playing cards and drinking.

I am not pleased with your conduct, Grant.

He soon became discouraged and unhappy, and longed to return to his family. He resigned from the army in April 1854.

28

For the next six years, Grant tried to make a living for his family. He farmed 60 acres of land owned by Julia in Missouri.

Grant had little success as a farmer. He moved to St. Louis to sell real estate.

This is a fine piece of land.

But not what I had in mind.

Selling real estate was also not for Grant. He joined his two brothers in Galena, Illinois to help run a store owned by their father.

And became friends with a political leader, John Rawlins.

You never talk about politics, Ulysses. How do you stand?

I'm not sure. But the talk I hear about Southern states leaving the Union disturbs me greatly.

29

The U.S. was deeply divided over the slavery issue. Northerners were angry over the passage of the Fugitive Slave Act—making it unlawful for anyone to help slaves who escaped to free territory.

Leave this man alone! He has done no harm!

He is a runaway slave. If you protect him, *you* will go to jail.

Southerners were angry when Kansas was admitted as a free state.

THE KANSAS GAZE

LARGEST ONE-CENT CIRCULATION

ANSAS ENTERS UNIO

AS A FREE STATE

ADMITTANCE OF KANSAS ANGERS THE SOUTH

VIOLENCE FEARED

Republican Abraham Lincoln was elected President in 1860. He made speeches that made Southerners more uneasy.

A house divided against itself cannot stand.

Angry and afraid after Lincoln's election, eleven Southern states quickly left the Union and formed their own government—the Confederate States of America.

Confederate soldiers fired on Union soldiers at Fort Sumter, South Carolina on April 12, 1861. The Civil War began.

President Lincoln asked for 75,000 volunteers.

VOLUNTEERS WANTED!

In Galena, Grant attended a town meeting where his friend John Rawlins made a stirring speech.

Republicans and Democrats must unite to preserve the Union!

Grant was shaken by the war. He felt it was his duty to go back into military service.

I must return to the army, Julia.

He organized a company of Galena volunteers and took them to Springfield.

U.S. ARMY

31

The next day, Illinois Governor Richard Yates requested that Grant meet with him.

I would like you to be my personal aide—in charge of all recruiting in Illinois.

A few months later, Yates named Grant colonel of the 21st Illinois Regiment.

The recruits are wild young men. They need discipline.

Grant worked hard training his unruly troops.

When I tell you to march, you will *march*! And when I tell you to halt, you will *halt*!

He was ordered to the town of Mexico, Missouri. Two new regiments were added to his command.

Promoted to brigadier general in 1861, Grant was given command of southern Illinois and southeastern Missouri.

Read the paper, sir! You're a general!

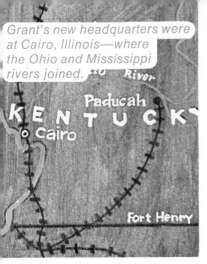

Grant's new headquarters were at Cairo, Illinois—where the Ohio and Mississippi rivers joined.

He appointed John Rawlins as his personal aide.

I believe whichever army controls the Mississippi River will win this war.

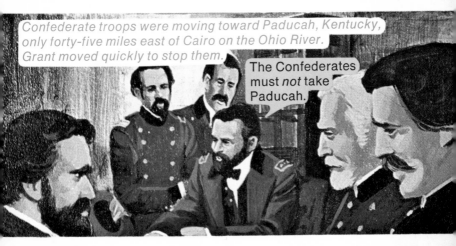

Confederate troops were moving toward Paducah, Kentucky, only forty-five miles east of Cairo on the Ohio River. Grant moved quickly to stop them.

The Confederates must *not* take Paducah.

He loaded two regiments of infantry and one battery of artillery onto transports at midnight—and started up the Ohio River.

They reached Paducah at dawn. The Confederate army, only a few miles away, withdrew quickly!

Grant was ordered to stop Confederate troops from crossing the Ohio River.

I'll stop them! I'll attack them at Belmont.

Surprised by Grant's attack at Belmont, the Confederate army ran for the river.

Look at them Rebels run!

But instead of following the retreating Confederates, Grant's men went wild. They looted the deserted camp.

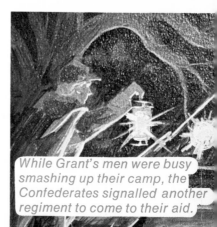

While Grant's men were busy smashing up their camp, the Confederates signalled another regiment to come to their aid.

Grant was afraid the stronger Confederate regiment could surround and cut off his soldiers from their ship. He and Rawlins set fire to the camp to get his men's attention.

Listen to your general, men! We're being attacked!

What'll we do? We can't get to our boat!

Fight your way back the same way you fought your way here!

Grant's men made it back to the boat, and Grant was the last man up the gangplank.

Two of the strongest Confederate positions were Fort Henry on the Tennessee River, and Fort Donelson on the Cumberland. Grant wanted to attack Fort Henry. After waiting impatiently for several weeks, he finally received permission.

It's from Major General Halleck. Tell the men we're moving out!

We're going to fight!

The soldiers were overjoyed; they were bored and wanted to get into the fight.

But when Grant's men reached Fort Henry, they found only a few Confederate soldiers —who quickly surrendered.

Send this message to Major General Halleck: Fort Henry is ours. I shall take and destroy Fort Donelson on February 8.

But Fort Donelson was well fortified against attack. 21,000 Confederate soldiers were waiting inside the fort.

Deep ravines filled with floodwaters ran along the fort on the north and south.

A long line of rifle pits was dug along the west side of the fort.

And heavy guns placed on the bluffs above the Cumberland River were aimed to destroy gunboats in the water below.

General Halleck wired Grant to wait for reinforcements before attacking. Grant either did not receive the message or refused to wait. He ordered an immediate attack!

Confederate guns firing from the bluffs, sank or disabled all of Grant's boats in the river.

And Confederate soldiers broke through Grant's advancing troops

Every Rebel soldier was wearing a pack on his back.

What?

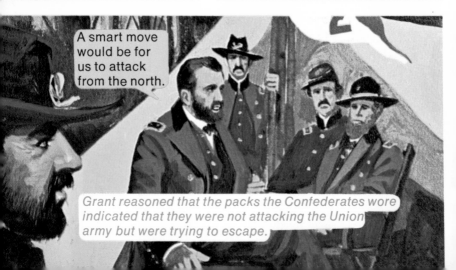

A smart move would be for us to attack from the north.

Grant reasoned that the packs the Confederates wore indicated that they were not attacking the Union army but were trying to escape.

Grant was right. The Confederates were trying to escape, By nightfall, Union soldiers were inside Fort Donelson. A note was delivered to Grant at dawn.

The Confederate general wants to know our peace terms.

Tell him: No terms except unconditional and immediate surrender.

Grant reported his victory to his superiors in Washington.

When word of Grant's victory at Fort Donelson reached President Lincoln, he sent a message to Congress.

I want U. S. Grant promoted to major general. Let's give him command of the Army of the Tennessee.

Grant was the new hero of the North. Soon, everyone talked about him and used his new nickname.

You know what the "U. S." in Grant's name stands for?

Sure. It means *Unconditional Surrender.*

39

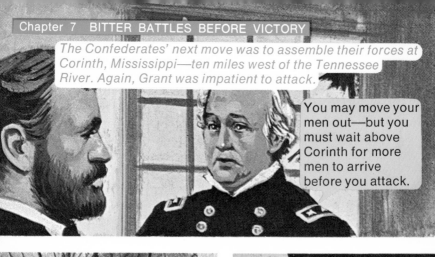

The Confederates' next move was to assemble their forces at Corinth, Mississippi—ten miles west of the Tennessee River. Again, Grant was impatient to attack.

You may move your men out—but you must wait above Corinth for more men to arrive before you attack.

Grant landed his army twenty miles north of Corinth. His men set up camp inland on a plateau near Shiloh Church.

Grant's old friend from West Point, William Sherman, arrived to take command of one of the Union divisions.

This could be a major battle of the war, Will. We must win.

When General Sherman noticed scared rabbits and deer running out of the forest at Shiloh, he knew that the Confederate army was on the move.

At dawn the next morning, the Confederates opened a fierce attack on Grant's army. The Union soldiers were scared. Grant rode up and down the lines trying to calm his men.

Both sides fought hard and bravely. By nightfall, the Shiloh plateau was covered with dead bodies.

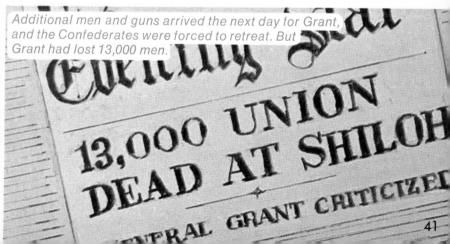

Additional men and guns arrived the next day for Grant, and the Confederates were forced to retreat. But Grant had lost 13,000 men.

Evening Star

13,000 UNION DEAD AT SHILOH

GENERAL GRANT CRITICIZED

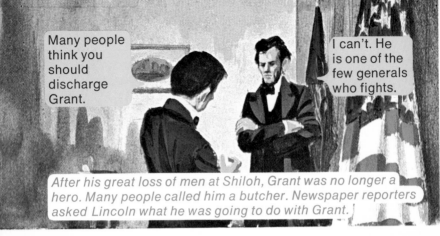

Many people think you should discharge Grant.

I can't. He is one of the few generals who fights.

After his great loss of men at Shiloh, Grant was no longer a hero. Many people called him a butcher. Newspaper reporters asked Lincoln what he was going to do with Grant.

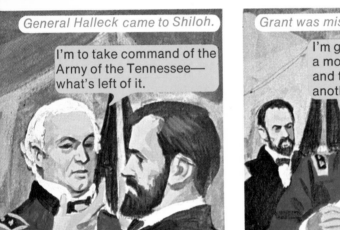

General Halleck came to Shiloh.

I'm to take command of the Army of the Tennessee— what's left of it.

Grant was miserable.

I'm going to ask for a month's leave— and then request another assignment.

Soon afterward, General Halleck was called to Washington to become commander in chief of the entire Union army. Grant was sent to Corinth to again take command of the Army of the Tennessee.

Do you think the Union can still win?

I *know* we can . . . if we can get control of the Mississippi River.

42

Grant went on to win brilliant victories at Vicksburg and at Chattanooga, Tennessee. Grant was given command of the entire Union army. Leaving Sherman in command of the Army of the West, he took personal charge of the Army of the Potomac.

Soldiers in the Army of the Potomac were not impressed by Grant.

The whole Union army is afraid of Lee. I fought with him in Mexico. He's a great leader, but he is not a god. He *can* be beaten.

Grant led his men out after Robert E. Lee on May 8, 1864. Lee's army was positioned near Chancellorsville, Virginia.

There is a 12-mile-square forest ahead called The Wilderness. We must move through that forest and south around Lee's army.

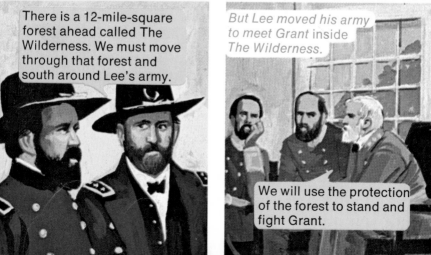

But Lee moved his army to meet Grant inside The Wilderness.

We will use the protection of the forest to stand and fight Grant.

Both sides fought hard. Thousands of men were killed. Neither side could claim victory. Grant told his men on May 7 to prepare to march.

Same old story . . . we fight Lee . . . we get killed . . . we retreat!

Forward!

Hey, we're not retreating as we thought! We're going after Lee!

Grant's and Lee's armies met and fought many bitter battles in The Wilderness. Lee had fewer men than Grant, but put up a strong defense. Grant moved toward Spotsylvania, Virginia. A fierce battle there lasted two weeks.

EXTRA

BUTCHER OF SHILOH RIDES AGAIN!

Lee moved south to Cold Harbor, Virginia. Grant's attack was driven back. He lost 12,000 men in one day.

Next, Grant aimed his army at Petersburg, Virginia. But Lee got to Petersburg first.

Grant doesn't stop—he just keeps attacking.

Grant had moved to Petersburg to try to cut off supplies going into Richmond.

We must attack Lee's defenses around Petersburg. We will dig trenches and keep him so busy fighting that he will not be able to get food into Richmond or supplies to his own army.

While Grant's army surrounded Petersburg, other Union armies began winning on different fronts. General Sherman drove his large army through Georgia to Atlanta. He began his march to the sea and destroyed all the crops and railroads in his path.

Admiral Farragut seized Mobile Bay, Alabama— a leading Southern port.

Union General Sheridan won a sweeping victory at the Shenandoah Valley in Virginia.

The North was overjoyed with the new Union victories. It showed its feelings by reelecting Lincoln in 1864 by more than 400,000 votes.

Lee will soon be surrounded by the armies of Sherman, Meade, Sheridan, and myself. I can't see how he can hold out very long.

Grant was right. Lee agreed to meet Grant at Appomattox on April 9 to discuss the terms of surrender.

Your men may keep their horses and return to their homes. But first they must sign a pledge to lay down their guns.

The Confederate soldiers went home. They were allowed to keep their own horses, mules, and only small guns.

47

Grant was invited to Washington on April 14 to meet with President Lincoln and his cabinet.

General Grant is here to help us plan ways to put our country back together again.

That same night, Lincoln and his wife went to Ford's Theater to see a play. John Wilkes Booth, a crazed actor and Southern sympathizer, rushed to the Lincoln box and shot Lincoln in the head.

Grant and his family were dining in a Philadelphia hotel when a messenger brought the tragic news.

Lincoln has been shot!

Lincoln died the next morning. Grant stood alone at the head of Lincoln's casket during the funeral.

The new President, Andrew Johnson, asked Grant to help him.

You are the most admired man in America now. I hope I may count on your help.

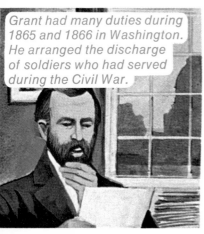

Grant had many duties during 1865 and 1866 in Washington. He arranged the discharge of soldiers who had served during the Civil War.

Congress promoted Grant to full general in July, 1866. He was the first to hold that rank since George Washington.

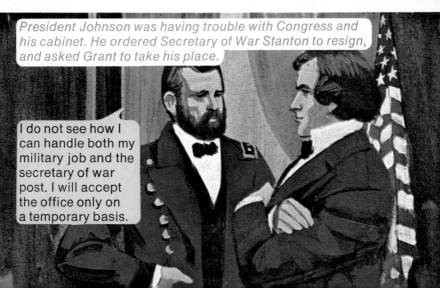

President Johnson was having trouble with Congress and his cabinet. He ordered Secretary of War Stanton to resign, and asked Grant to take his place.

I do not see how I can handle both my military job and the secretary of war post. I will accept the office only on a temporary basis.

Congress was angry at President Johnson and demanded that Stanton be returned to his office. Grant refused to be caught in the political crossfire, and resigned his new job.

I refuse to go against the wishes of Congress.

You have gone back on your word to me.

Six months later, on May 20, 1868, the Republicans nominated Grant to run for President.

GRANT LEADER

GRANT LEADER IN WAR LEADER IN PEACE

Many people favored Grant.

He hasn't had any experience in politics.

He's a leader, and that's what we need now.

Grant defeated the Democratic candidate, Horatio Seymour, by more than 300,000 votes.

I've just received word, Julia. I'm afraid I am elected.

Grant became President during one of the most difficult times in America's history. Many believed the country would reunite quickly if the South received fair treatment. But radical Republicans in Congress demanded that the South be punished.

No man who served the Confederacy in any way should be allowed to hold a public office.

The new Fifteenth Amendment to the Constitution allowed blacks to vote for the first time. But some angry whites formed the secret Ku Klux Klan and tried to stop them.

Grant ordered that members of the Ku Klux Klan be hunted down and jailed. But the task was great.

We have captured many members of the Klan and sent them to prison. But it will take years to end this terrible evil.

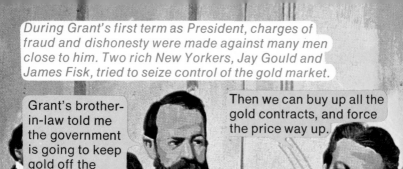

During Grant's first term as President, charges of fraud and dishonesty were made against many men close to him. Two rich New Yorkers, Jay Gould and James Fisk, tried to seize control of the gold market.

Grant's brother-in-law told me the government is going to keep gold off the market until fall.

Then we can buy up all the gold contracts, and force the price way up.

We're ruined! How could the government let this happen?

When Grant learned what Gould and Fisk were trying to do, he ordered the release of $4 million in government gold. But people who had invested in gold stocks lost heavily when gold prices went down—instead of up as expected.

Grant was proud of American industry when the first transcontinental railroad was completed on May 10, 1869.

But he was shocked when he learned that his own vice-president and some members of Congress had accepted shares of railroad stock in return for political favors.

People can't blame *you*.

But they *do*.

Grant had many proposals on foreign policy. But he failed to win support of Congress to gain his goals. In 1869, the leaders of the Dominican Republic offered to sell their country to the United States.

It's a good opportunity. Perhaps ex-slaves would want to live there and set up new states.

Without consulting his cabinet, Grant sent his personal aide to draw up papers annexing the Dominican Republic to the United States.

When the aide returned with a treaty to annex the island, Charles Sumner and other leaders in the Senate were against the plan.

The annexation treaty was not approved by Congress.

I can lead an army better than I can a nation.

But he gained some of his other goals. England agreed to pay the U.S. $15 million for supplying the Confederacy with warships during the Civil War.

Grant signed a law providing for an eight-hour workday for all government employees.

And America's first national park was created at Yellowstone, Montana in 1872.

Grant won a second term by defeating Horace Greeley. His inauguration on March 4, 1873 drew thousands of people.

I have been the subject of abuse and slander . . . but I consider my reelection proof of my vindication.

More trouble followed Grant during his second term. America suffered a financial panic in 1873. Hundreds of banks and businesses closed.

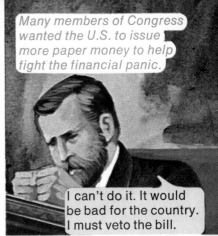

Many members of Congress wanted the U.S. to issue more paper money to help fight the financial panic.

I can't do it. It would be bad for the country. I must veto the bill.

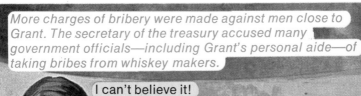

More charges of bribery were made against men close to Grant. The secretary of the treasury accused many government officials—including Grant's personal aide—of taking bribes from whiskey makers.

I can't believe it!

The whiskey makers wanted their production records changed so they would pay less taxes.

When Grant learned that his secretary of war had received payoffs from the sale of Indian trading posts, he ordered him to quit.

I offer you my resignation.

I am afraid I must accept it.

Grant did not run for a third term. He and Julia left on a trip around the world in May, 1877.

They were cheered by thousands everywhere. Heads of state entertained them in every country they visited.

They were delighted by the people living in China and the Far East.

The Grants returned to the U.S. in 1879. They had traveled for two and a half years.

We met the leaders of almost every country in the world. But I'm glad to be home, Ulysses.

The Grants moved to New York. He opened a banking firm, with his son and Ferdinand Ward as partners. At first, the firm was successful. But Ward came to see Grant on a Sunday evening in May, 1884.

We must raise $150,000 to pay a large city draft, and we do not have the money.

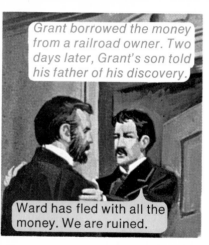

Grant borrowed the money from a railroad owner. Two days later, Grant's son told his father of his discovery.

Ward has fled with all the money. We are ruined.

Grant paid back the money by giving the lender acres of land he and Julia owned.

We have no money left. I must find a way to support us.

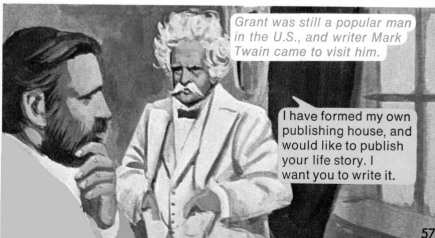

Grant was still a popular man in the U.S., and writer Mark Twain came to visit him.

I have formed my own publishing house, and would like to publish your life story. I want you to write it.

It was while Grant was writing his memoirs that he learned he did not have long to live.

I'm sorry, Ulysses. You have cancer of the throat.

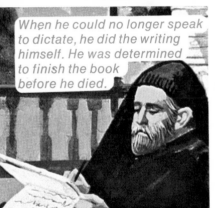

When he could no longer speak to dictate, he did the writing himself. He was determined to finish the book before he died.

Grant finished his Memoirs on July 19. Four days later, on July 23, 1885, he died.

LET US HAVE PEACE

Twelve years later, on April 27, 1897, President McKinley dedicated Grant's Tomb in New York City in his respected memory.

Important Places in the Life of U.S. Grant

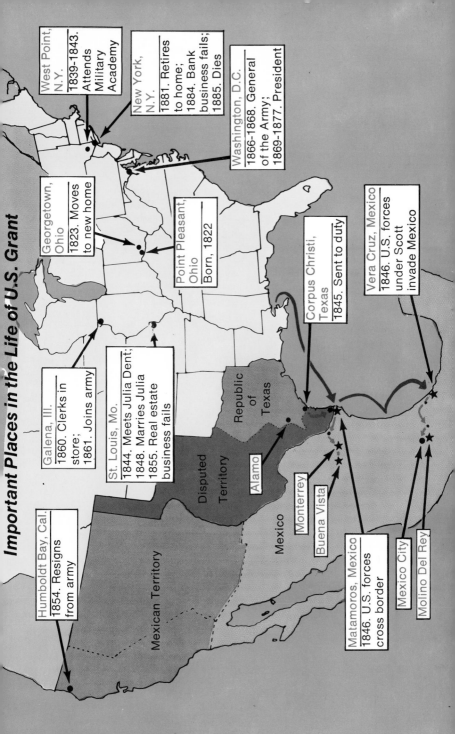

West Point, N.Y.
1839-1843. Attends Military Academy

New York, N.Y.
1881. Retires to home; 1884. Bank business fails; 1885. Dies

Washington, D.C.
1866-1868. General of the Army; 1869-1877. President

Georgetown, Ohio
1823. Moves to new home

Point Pleasant, Ohio
Born, 1822

Corpus Christi, Texas
1845. Sent to duty

Vera Cruz, Mexico
1846. U.S. forces under Scott invade Mexico

Galena, Ill.
1860. Clerks in store; 1861. Joins army

St. Louis, Mo.
1844. Meets Julia Dent; 1848. Marries Julia 1855. Real estate business fails

Humboldt Bay, Cal.
1854. Resigns from army

Republic of Texas

Alamo

Disputed Territory

Mexico

Mexican Territory

Monterrey

Buena Vista

Matamoros, Mexico
1846. U.S. forces cross border

Mexico City

Molino Del Rey

59

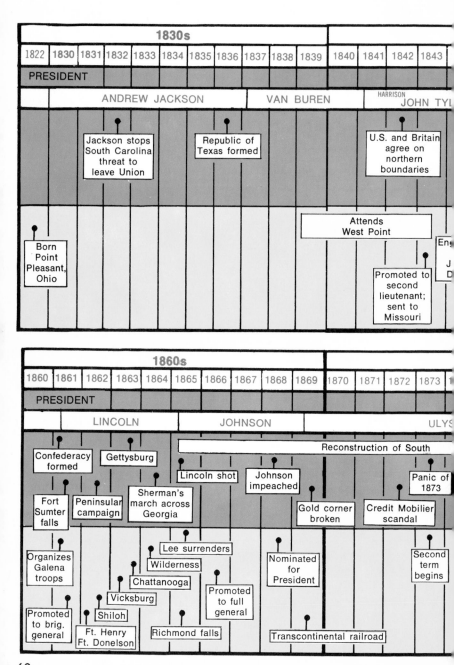

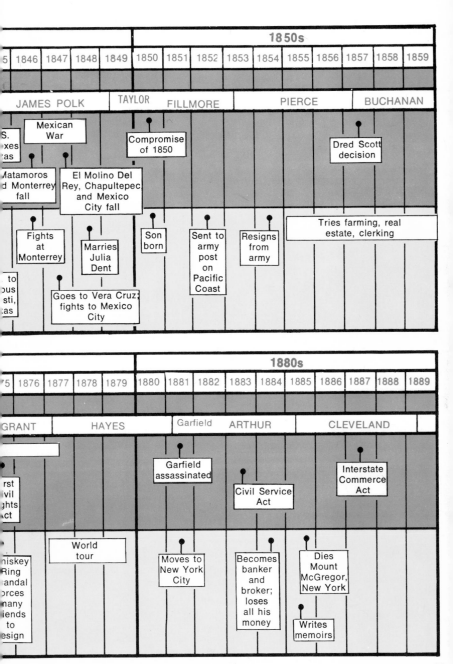

	1850s													
5	1846	1847	1848	1849	1850	1851	1852	1853	1854	1855	1856	1857	1858	1859

JAMES POLK   TAYLOR   FILLMORE   PIERCE   BUCHANAN

S.
xes
as

Mexican War

Compromise of 1850

Dred Scott decision

Matamoros
d Monterrey fall

El Molino Del Rey, Chapultepec, and Mexico City fall

to
ous
sti,
as

Fights at Monterrey

Marries Julia Dent

Son born

Sent to army post on Pacific Coast

Resigns from army

Tries farming, real estate, clerking

Goes to Vera Cruz; fights to Mexico City

	1880s													
5	1876	1877	1878	1879	1880	1881	1882	1883	1884	1885	1886	1887	1888	1889

GRANT   HAYES   Garfield   ARTHUR   CLEVELAND

rst
vil
ghts
ct

Garfield assassinated

Civil Service Act

Interstate Commerce Act

hiskey
Ring
andal
rces
any
iends
to
esign

World tour

Moves to New York City

Becomes banker and broker; loses all his money

Dies Mount McGregor, New York

Writes memoirs

61

GLOSSARY

The meanings and pronunciations of words found in this book.

admitted *(ăd-mĭt'ĕd)*
allowed to enter or join

ammunition *(ăm-yə-nĭsh'ən)*
explosive materials for guns

annexation *(ăn-ĕk-sā'shən)*
the act of joining or adding on

Appomattox *(ăp-ə-măt'əks)*
village in Virginia in which Lee surrendered to Grant

artillery *(är-tĭl'ər-ē)*
large, heavy, shell-firing weapons such as cannons, howitzers, or naval guns

barracks *(băr'ĭks)*
a building or group of buildings used to house soldiers

batteries *(băt'ə-rēz)*
prepared positions where heavy guns are set up

belfry *(bĕl'frē)*
a tower or steeple in which one or more bells are hung

bombard *(bŏm-bärd')*
to attack repeatedly with bombs, shells, or missiles

bribe *(brīb)*
money or favor given—or promised—for influence

cadets *(kə-dĕts')*
students training to be officers at a military school

Civil War *(sĭv'əl wôr)*
the war (1861-1865) between the Union (North) and the Confederacy (South)

commander *(kə-măn'dər)*
the chief commissioned officer of a military unit

commission *(kə-mĭsh'ən)*
an official document giving a rank and authority to a member of the armed forces

Confederates *(kən-fĕd'ər-ĭts)*
Southerners during the Civil War

Congress *(kŏng'grĭs)*
the elected representatives from all states in the U.S.; the two bodies, the Senate and the House of Representatives

congressman *(kŏng'grĭs-mən)*
a member of the U.S. Congress

Democrats *(dĕm'ə-krats)*
members of one of the political parties in the United States

depot *(dē'pō)*
a place for storing or repairing military equipment and materials

engagement *(ĕn-gāj'mənt)*
promise to marry

financial *(fĭ-năn'shəl)*
having to do with money matters

Fort Sumter *(fôrt sŭm'tər)*
the fort in South Carolina where Confederate soldiers first fired on Union soldiers

forward *(fôr'wərd)*
a word used by an officer in battle to urge his troops onward

fugitive *(fyōō'jə-tĭv)*
one who is fleeing from justice or the law; a runaway

gangplank *(găng'plăngk)*
a removable board or plank used as a footway between a ship and a pier

governor *(gŭv'ər-nər)*
chief executive of a state in the U.S.

graduation *(grăj-ōō-ā'shən)*
a ceremony at which a student receives a diploma showing completion of studies

haze *(hāz)*
to play pranks—sometimes rough and hurting a person's pride—on a newcomer

horseman *(hôrs'mən)*
a man skilled at riding a horse

howitzer *(hou'ĭt-sər)*
a cannon that fires shells in a high pattern to fall on targets

infantry *(ĭn'fən-trē)*
soldiers trained to fight on foot

leather tanning *(lĕth'ər tăn'ĭng)*
the process or method of making leather from animal hides

livery stable *(lĭv'ə-rē stā'bəl)*
place where horses are boarded or kept for hire with carriages

organized *(ôr'gə-nīzd)*
joined or formed into an unit or group

GLOSSARY

panic-stricken *(păn'ĭk-strĭk-ən)*
overcome by panic; terrified

plateau *(plă-tō')*
an area of flat land higher than surrounding land

pontoon *(pŏn-tōon')*
a flat-bottomed boat or other structure used to support a floating bridge

Rebels *(rĕb'əls)*
Southerners during Civil War; persons who refuse loyalty to an established government

recruits *(rĭ-krōots')*
new, untrained members of a military unit

regiment *(rĕj'ə-mənt)*
a military unit of ground troops made up of several smaller units

registered *(rĕj'ĭ-stərd)*
officially enrolled or listed

Republicans *(rĭ-pŭb'lĭ-kəns)*
members of one of the political parties in the U.S.

request *(rĭ-kwĕst')*
to ask for something

resigned *(rĭ-zīnd')*
gave up a job or position

retreat *(rĭ-trēt')*
to go backward; withdraw

reveal *(rĭ-vēl')*
to make known what had been secret

rhythm *(rĭth'əm)*
a sound pattern formed by long or short notes like heavy and soft beats on a drum

Senate *(sĕn'ĭt)*
the highest group of lawmakers in the country

siege *(sēj)*
the surrounding and blockading of a town or fortress by an attacking army

subscription *(səb-skrĭp'shən)*
a signed pledge of payment for a child's schooling

surrendered *(sə-rĕn'dərd)*
gave up to an enemy

tannery *(tăn'ər-ē)*
a place where hides are made into leather

temporary *(tĕm'pə-rĕr-ē)*
not permanent; for a limited time

territory *(tĕr'ə-tôr-ē)*
an area of land under the control of a nation or ruler

theater *(thē'ə-tər)*
building or large room where plays, pictures, and other events are staged. President and Mrs. Lincoln went to a play at Ford's *Theater.*

transcontinental
(trăns-kŏn-tə-nĕn'təl)
crossing America from coast to coast

trenches *(trĕn'chĕz)*
long, narrow ditches used to protect soldiers in warfare

unconditional surrender
(ŭn-kən-dĭsh'ən-əl sə-rĕn'dər)
giving up to an enemy without any special terms

Union *(yōon'yən)*
the North during the Civil War

vindication *(vĭn-dĭ-kā'shən)*
the evidence or event that serves to clear of blame or doubt

volunteered *(vŏl-ən-tĭrd')*
gave service or performed of his own free will

West Point
site of the U.S. Military Academy in southeastern New York

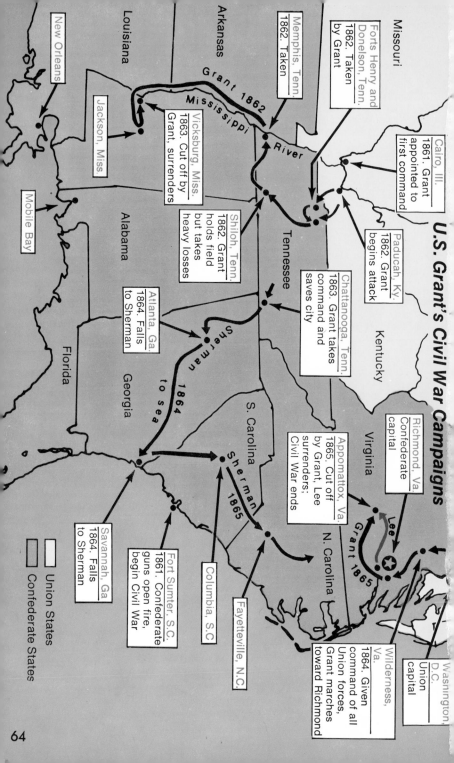

U.S. Grant's Civil War Campaigns

New Orleans

Louisiana

Arkansas

Missouri

Forts Henry and
Donelson, Tenn.
1862. Taken
by Grant

Memphis, Tenn.
1862. Taken

Grant 1862

Mississippi River

Jackson, Miss

Vicksburg, Miss.
1863. Grant, cut off by
Grant, surrenders
but takes
heavy losses

Mobile Bay

Alabama

Shiloh, Tenn.
1862. Grant
holds field
but takes
heavy losses

Tennessee

Cairo, Ill.
1861. Grant
appointed to
first command

Paducah, Ky.
1862. Grant
begins attack

Chattanooga, Tenn.
1863. Grant takes
command and
saves city

Kentucky

Atlanta, Ga.
1864. Falls
to Sherman

Sherman to sea 1864

Florida

Georgia

S. Carolina

Sherman 1865

Richmond, Va.
Confederate
capital

Virginia

Appomattox, Va.
1865. Cut off
by Grant, Lee
surrenders;
Civil War ends

N. Carolina

Grant 1865

Lee

Savannah, Ga
1864. Falls
to Sherman

Columbia, S.C

Fort Sumter, S.C.
1861. Confederate
guns open fire,
begin Civil War

Fayetteville, N.C.

Washington,
D.C.
Union capital

Wilderness,
Va.
1864. Given
command of all
Union forces,
Grant marches
toward Richmond

Union States
Confederate States

Union States
Confederate States

64